There's a Hippo in My Locker

and other humorous poems

by Jeff Nathan

Illustrated by Jillian Nathan

A Chucklebook

www.chucklebooks.com

There's a Hippo in my Locker
Copyright © 2000 by Jeff Nathan

First Edition 2000

10 9 8 7 6 5 4 3

ISBN 0-9702730-0-2

Library of Congress Card Number: 00-106046

Published by Chucklebooks Publishing, Inc.
P.O. Box 1052◆Andover, MA 01810◆(978) 749-0674
www.chucklebooks.com

ATTENTION: EDUCATIONAL INSTITUTIONS AND FUNDRAISERS: Quantity discounts are available on bulk purchases of this book for reselling, educational purposes, gifts, or fund-raising. Customized books or book excerpts can also be created for specific purposes. For specific information, please contact: Chucklebooks Sales Department
                                          PO Box 1052, Andover, MA 01810
                                          phone: 978-749-0674

Publisher's Cataloging-in-Publication
(Provided by Quality Books, Inc.)

Nathan, Jeffrey.
    There's a hippo in my locker : and other humorous poems / by Jeff Nathan ; illustrated by Jillian Nathan. -- 1st ed.
        p. cm.
    LCCN: 00-106046
    ISBN: 0-9702730-0-2

    1. Children's poetry, American.   I. Nathan, Jillian.   II. Title.

PS3564.A8436T44 2000   811.6
                    QBI00-500086

Acknowledgments

A big "thank you" to those who have helped me get this, my first book, published.

Thanks to the Merrimack Junior Theater for giving me a reason to start writing the poems in the first place, and also for convincing me to publish them.

I'm especially grateful to Ronel Kelmen, Eileen Nathan, Claudia Richards, and Keith Richards for their editing help.

Gallons of appreciation go out to Nancy McGloin for providing the back-up plan for the illustrations and making it possible for Jill to complete them.

A loving thank you goes to my daughter, Jill, for the really cute artwork.

And a loving thank you to my wife, Jackie, who has been chief sounding board and who has taken on my share of the work at home while I put the book together.

For Shayna, Craig, Brendon, and Jill.
                              -JDN

How to Contact the Author

Speaker, singer, songwriter, poet, and author Jeff Nathan is often available to bring his fun and wit to you. To discuss hiring him for your next conference, fund-raiser, special event, or school assembly or workshop, contact:

Jeff Nathan
Chucklebooks Publishing
P.O. Box 1052
Andover, MA 01810

e-mail: jeff@chucklebooks.com
Phone: 978-749-0674

Table of Contents

There's a Hippo in My Locker

There's a hippo in my locker and he's quite the hefty dude.
He's lounging on my notebook with his bag of hippo food.

Don't ask me to unlock it – I want to stay alive.
When he comes out and tramples me no way would I survive.

I can not get my homework – he might destroy the school.
Oh, please don't send me back there. How could you be so cruel?

He's big and mean and ugly with a big horn on his head,
And a t-shirt that says "Hippo" – if I open it I'm dead.

What's that you say? A hippo has no horn upon its head?
Uh – There's a rhino in my locker. Didn't you hear what I said?

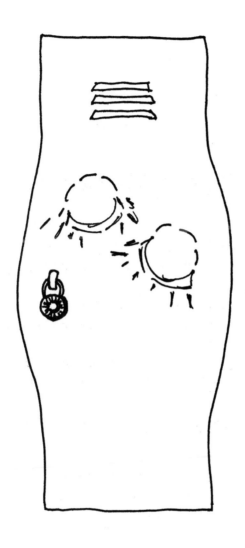

The Thief

So, where were you last evening when the evil deed was done?
Do you have a criminal record? Have you ever owned a gun?

You refuse to say you did it, but I've proven that's the truth,
'Cause I'm the master of detectives, a pretty crafty sleuth.

My birthday cake is gone from the refrigerator shelf.
You pretend you didn't know, yet you took it for yourself.

I was shocked to find out YOU had been behind this situation.
You're supposed to be so righteous – after all, you're a Dalmatian!

But the evidence will prove you're not that innocent little fellow.
There was dog hair in the butter! There were paw prints in the jello!

Did you know that you were spotted at the scene of the crime?
(Well, that doesn't really matter 'cause you're spotted all the time.)

I've determined that you're guilty, have you any last requests?
Why ARE you laying down now? Oh, I see – the defense rests.

You'll be rather stiffly punished, it was such a heinous crime,
And what a mess you left so let the punishment fit the grime!

But you won't be doing solitary – not like I was hopin',
'Cause mom caught your accomplice – I left the fridge wide open.

A Tough Battle

I've just returned from the most intensive battle.
It's a miserable, bitterly fought war.
We were up against a force we couldn't rattle.
They outnumbered us by a hundred men or more.

And just when we're about to be surrounded,
We found a path to sneak right through their line.
We had just about escaped when they found it,
And came after us - just a step or two behind.

We ran until our legs - they felt like jelly.
We finally lost them, but we all were hurt.
And stress like that - it gets ya in the belly.
So, Dad, that's why I need some more dessert.

Katie Zimmerman's Torture

Oh please don't make me do it.
I promise I'll be good.
I'll clean my room and vacuum –
I'll do everything I should.

There is no form of torture
So inhumane and cruel,
As forcing me to practice
The piano after school.

I can't believe you're actually
Treating me this way.
I know I practiced last time,
Just 3 weeks ago, today.

The bench is so uncomf'table.
The keys just don't seem level.
The sound that comes out when I play
Could even scare the devil!

So, tell ya what – let's make a deal
In good supportive spirit:
You don't make me play this thing,
And I won't make you hear it.

The Egg Poem

An egg is something rather odd:
A blob in semi-round façade.

It has a light protective shell
That can't protect it very well.

Where were all the bad eggs sent?
Into eggs-ile's where they went.

Need to make a small egg great?
Why, friend, you must eggs-aggerate.

How'd you send an egg away?
Use the eggs-it, s'il vous plait.

What's the smartest egg – bar none?
That would be the eggs-pert one.

Do you want to show eggs how?
Do it by eggs-ample, now.

Outspoken eggs aren't hard to spot.
They're eggs-troverts, are they not?

How to give an egg elation?
Just pour on some egg-saltation.

How d'you rid what's in the shell?
An eggs-orcist should do that well.

Don't like an egg? Think it's strange?
Take it back for an even eggs-change.

My egg poem's done now. That is it -
Unless you egg me on a bit.

Wait For Me

Please don't walk so fast,
Wait for me, wait for me.
I hate your moving past,
Wait for me, wait for me.

I try to keep up, can't you see?
But I can barely reach your knee
'Cause, after all, I'm only 3.
Won't you please wait for me?

Vacuum

How do you spell vacuum?
A trivial word.
But not when I wrote out
Just what I heard.

Then I caught the problem
From which it did stem:
I heard it as v – a – c –
W – m.

Back to School

The weekend's almost over.
The consequence is cruel.
When I wake up on Monday,
Must I go back to school?

Ain't no-one in the school
That speaks more better grammar.
And I know all the states from
Mrs. Pee to Alabamer.

I can find the root words
And put a prefix after.
You ask about word useage?
Ha - don't make me laughter.

I know a semi-colon
Is a kind of punctual mark.
And it rained for 30 days
'Fore Noah built an ... aardvark.

Spelling's been a breeze
Since I learned my abd's,
But, when I say anything,
It's ME all the kids tease.

From kids in my classes
Do I get just one kind word?
I swear, next year, I'm gonna
Teach first grade instead of third.

Megan Richards' Bake Sale

I usu'lly love bake sales.
You, normally, can't beat 'em.
'Cause, normally, I find the two best things
And quickly eat 'em.

But this bake sale is different;
It's not so fun today.
I'm selling at this bake sale
Sending all this stuff away.

The brownies look delicious.
We're down to only four.
Just sold the last three cookies -
I can't take it anymore.

Hey, Lady, drop that creampuff!
Whatever's left I'll buy,
Right after I devour
This croissant and apple pie.

I'll just eat two more fudge squares
And one last piece of cake.
I usu'lly love bake sales -
Just not the stomach-ache.

My Beautiful Car

My car is just
A perfect set of lines.
And don't you love
The way the engine whines?

Just notice how
It sparkles in the sun.
Come view my car –
What could be more fun?

Now, why waste time
Admiring for a minute?
Because I must –
My car keys are locked in it.

My Older Brother

I have an older brother and
He's really quite the pain.
Everything he does is meant
For driving me insane.

He'll use the same old chant to
Criticize all things I do.
He lifts his arms and yells, "Hey, dummy,
What is wrong with you?"

He hangs around to bother me
On each and every day.
I know he lives here also, but
Why can't he run away?

Last Friday night I tried to sleep.
I tossed and turned in bed.
List'ning to his handball pounding
Right above my head.

And when I thought his antics couldn't
Get any more lowly,
At 6 AM he screams to me,
"Wake up and be my goalie!"

This morning something strange occurred;
I thought I must be dreaming.
My brother - he was nice to me.
I wonder what he's scheming.

He shared his favorite gum and let
Me have an extra stick.
He helped me with my schoolbag -
My gosh, he must be sick!

So all that stuff I said 'bout how
I want to see him leaving -
I'm taking it all back ---
At least until this evening.

Fingernails

Why do we have fingernails?
They don't do much for me.
My sister's always painting hers.
Why can't she let them be?

It's hard to keep them really small.
They're always breaking when I fall.
They're in the way for basketball.
Can they help type? No, not at all.

Today I found out what they're for,
Now I don't want to lose them.
I was at the classroom board
And then I got to use them.

Down the chalkboard's front they plow.
They make a screeching shrill meow.
Their use has been discovered now
To make the girls all have a cow.

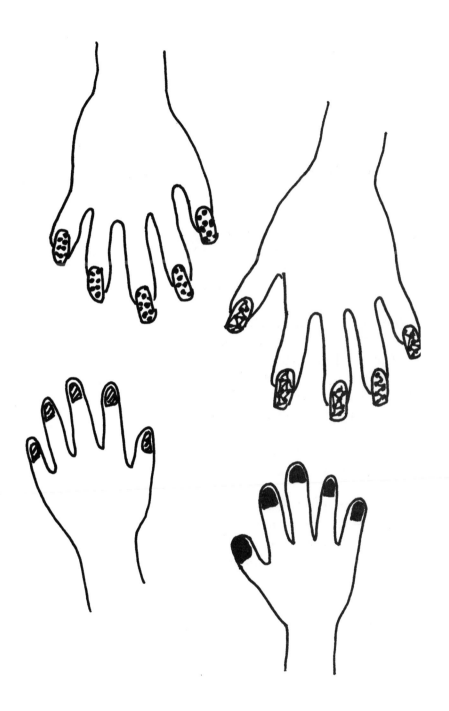

I'm Not Afraid of the Dark

I'm not afraid of the dark.
It isn't really scary.
It's just – if you're not wary
Something might be hiding there.

I really don't need the light
But still, I always use it,
'Cause if I ever lose it
I get this feeling in my hair.

So, please stop closing the door,
Once I'm in bed for sleeping.
I need to see things creeping,
And be constantly aware.

I'm not afraid of the dark.
Not even for a minute.
It's all the monsters in it
That are giving me this scare.

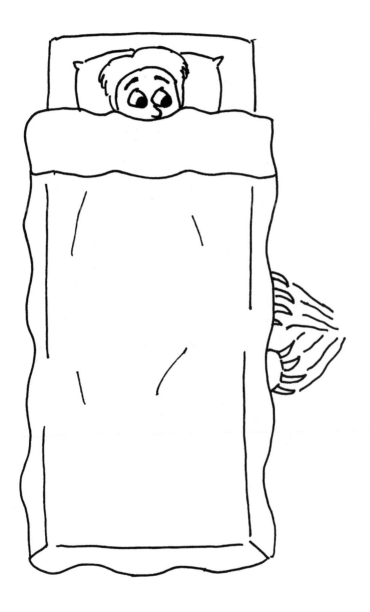

Doggie Troubles

I don't like my doggie 'cause he's always causin' trouble.
He steals my favorite shoes. He chews my Double Bubble.
Always making noise, when he's not barking loud, he yips.
He comes to lick my face and gets his slobber on my lips!

I don't like my doggie 'cause he's really very rude.
I wash my hands for dinner and he's eaten all my food.
I go to watch my TV shows - he beats me to MY chair.
Then he finds my favorite clothes and leaves behind his hair.

I don't like my doggie 'cause he gets me all upset.
He yelps when he hears thunder - he's such a needy pet!
But, today, when he got lost - he really made me cry.
I don't like my doggie 'cause I LOVE him, that's why.

The Anchovy

When it comes to pleasing me
There's no food like the anchovy.
It's my fav'rite, yesiree,
That tasty moustache from the sea.

A little brown mush comes and greets a-
Nother mouthful from my pizza.

Salty strips make eating fun.
Of all seafood, they're number one.

But why do females get this trophy?
With Aunt should be Unclechovy.

Jumbled Thoughts

I like to solve the jumbled words in papers' puzzle sections.
I think and try and test and write without reading directions.
I'll make up words in disarray,
Like TERBET once, and BREETT next day
But I have fun and that's okay,
'Cause my word's BETTER, anyway.

Lisa Harney's Annoyance

Middle school is loads of fun.
It's great just seeing everyone.
A world of learning, joy, and noise,
To make it perfect - lose the boys.

Boys are a crude and nasty sort.
You don't hear females spit and snort.
And can a boy just calmly sit?
He bounces - like an idiot.

I'm sick of getting stepped-on toes
And frogs put on my brand new clothes.
I don't like getting my hair yanked
And I don't like my fanny spanked.

I guess we're stuck - they're all around.
Most are slith'ring underground.
If it's with boys that we must live,
Give me handcuffs – and a sedative.

My Mom

My mom sometimes does things that are really off-the-wall
Like making me try on RED PANTS when we were at the mall.

She's chaperoning our upcoming dance next week – oh, brother!
Chaperoning's s'posed to be for someone else's mother.

Her broken arm from roller skating got to me last spring.
She had the nerve to pick me up at school wearing a sling!

When I grow up and have a kid,
To her, I won't do what mom did.
I won't make her try red pants.
I won't chaperone her dance.
I won't ever make her late.
I won't try to roller skate.
I will NEVER wear a sling.
Boy, moms can be embarrassing!

Soccer Ball Dance

I like to do the soccer ball dance.
Last time I fell on the seat of my pants.
But I scored 3 goals against a team of ants
'Cause I like to do the soccer ball dance.

Do the soccer ball dance
But don't use your hands.
Do the soccer ball dance.
Soccer gonna make me strong.

I bounce the ball on my head and knee.
I can strike it off the wall or over a tree.
I like kicking the ball this way, you see,
'Cause it sure beats having the ball kick me.

Do the soccer ball dance
But don't use your hands.
Do the soccer ball dance.
Soccer to me all day long.

A Geographic Meal

I'm **Hungary** right before my meal,
And boy, this hunger sure **Israel**,
So, time now, to get **China** for the table.
A **Cuba** sugar in my tea,
Turkey's the first food for me,
And then it's time for **Chile**, if I'm able.

Iraq of ribs, **Japan**-fried steak,
Just how much more food can I take
Before I'll fin'lly have to drop my fork?
I'll have this **danish** - one more piece,
With **french** fries just pulled from the **Greece**.
And don't forget the **Sweden** sour pork.

"Quickly, now", said an old man,
"**Russia** over here" and so **Iran**,
As that stuffed and bloated feeling gripped me.
The man told me he had a cure,
"**Italy**'s this **Spain**, for sure."
I bought some of his pills but, gosh, **Egypt** me.

So, doubled over from the pain,
It isn't fair that I complain;
Common sense is more of what I'm needing.
Instead of gorging like a dummy,
I could use this rule of thumby:
"You should never travel while you're eating."

The Birthday Present

I just opened the coolest birthday present ever made.
I started kinda slowly 'cause, at first, I was afraid.
But, finally, I got the nerve to open up the box,
And when I peeked inside I thought, "Hey, dude, this present rocks."

It's all these different colors mixed with angles, wings, and fins.
It whirls and turns and rolls and flips and flops and flies and spins.
Boy, this birthday present really turned out mighty fine.
Too bad I don't know what it is - too bad it isn't mine.

Six Cents More

I finally saved up the 99 cents
To pay for a Pervish Gumhiat
I got some tough chores done for all of my friends
And now I could finally buy it.

So, up to the counter I strode with my prize.
Put my 99 cents 'fore the shopkeeper's eyes.
She said, "Son, this is bad news, but these are the facts:
You've got everything here but the tax."

Six cents more,
Is exactly what you must bring.
Six cents more,
If you want this wretched thing.

But I swept up for Tom and I painted at Lenny's.
For another 6 cents, I don't think I can do more.
Wait – I've got six cents – instead of six pennies,
Perhaps you can take my six cents of humor.

Six cents more,
Is exactly what you must bring.
Six cents more,
If you want this wretched thing.

You don't understand, I've been trying forever
And now I'm so close I don't know what to do.
This scrimping and saving, oh, what an endeavor.
Can City Hall please take an I.O.U. ?

Six cents more,
Is exactly what you must bring.
Six cents more,
If you want this wretched thing.

So, I had to leave in a bit of a pickle.
My eyes to the pavement, I went out the door.
When what did I spy but a penny and nickel.
I scooped them right up and went back to the store.

Six cents more,
Is exactly what you must bring.
Six cents more,
If you want this wretched thing.

I told the store clerk I was back for the toy and
She said she was sorry but she had no more.
If I really wanted that wretched annoyance,
I must bring my money to some other store.

Six cents more,
Is exactly what you must bring.
Six cents more,
If you want this wretched thing.

So I hustled over to "Hobby and Pleasure".
They had what I wanted and I could relax.
Up on the counter the clerk put the treasure
And said it was one dollar five plus the tax.

Six cents more,
Is exactly what you must bring.
Six cents more,
If you want this wretched thing.

The Test Interruption

I know you don't want to be interrupted.
I know we're supposed to finish this test.
I'm sorry for having to come up and see you,
I really don't mean to be such a pest.

But, you see, my alarm didn't go off this morning,
My hair is uncombed, never got my face clean.
I flew into class with just half of my clothes on,
The victim of missing my morning routine.

I never ate breakfast, the bus left without me,
Forgetting my books was the cause of much strife.
But I think that not stopping off at the bathroom,
Just may be the biggest regret of my life.

I doubt that my legs can cross any harder.
The force is so strong my midsection is bowed.
I can't be responsible if I'm held captive.
There's just a few seconds before I explode.

What do you mean, "The test is all over"?
So now I can go do what I need to do?
Yahoo! See ya later. I'm off to the bathroom,
Before something else is all over, too.

My Pet Elephant

I have a dog, I have a cat,
I can't have any more than that.
My mom is glad my quota has been spent,
Because I yet want one more pet –
I'll get the bestest animal yet
And I will bring her home an elephant.

Oh, please, Mom, can I keep him?
He'll be the greatest pet.
He followed me from school today,
He's as big as he can get.
They're great for transportation,
If it's okay to go slow.
He's very good at washing cars –
That's something you should know.

And if there's something huge to move, you know you're
                                    gonna need him.
The cost for taking care of him? Its just peanuts to feed him.
He'll stay in the garage – until we have another plan.
If anybody asks us – he's a big new gray sedan.

Oh, please, Mom, can I keep him?
He can mow the lawn.
I really need him here – he'll be
My friend from tusk to dawn.
Life is so unfair sometimes –
Forgive me while I grieve.
My mom has told me I must make him
Pack his trunk and leave.

Nursery Fun-rhymes

Peter, Peter pumpkin-eater,
Had a wife and couldn't keep her.
He put her in a pumpkin shell,
And there, his wife, she sure did smell.

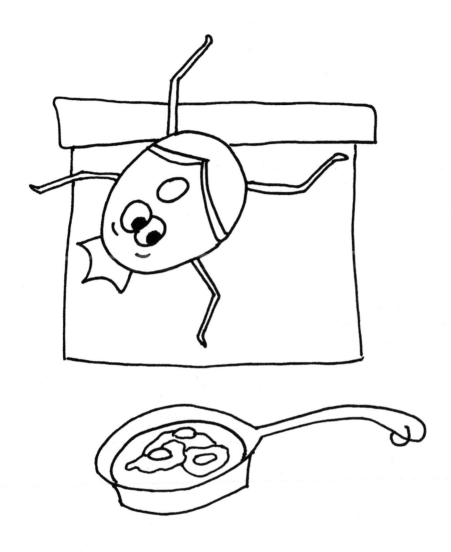

Humpty Dumpty sat on a wall
Humpty Dumpty had a great fall
All the king's horses and all the king's men
Quickly sat down for a big omelet then.

Nursery Un-rhymes

Little Miss Muffet, sat on a tuffet
Eating her curds and whey,
Along came a spider and sat down beside her,
So she squashed him with her spoon.

Little Miss Muffet, sat on a tuffet
Eating her curds and whey,
Along came a spider and sat down beside her,
So she ate him too.

•

Skunk Chasing

Once upon a sunny day,
I tried to chase a skunk away.
"To the woods – be gone", I say.
"And as you go, please don't spray."

The skunk, he sprayed, then stayed a spell
And me – I couldn't stand the smell.
For chasing skunks, now, I can tell
That I don't do that very well.

Foreign

Let's discuss a very foreign word,
For in it foreign letters go unheard.

There are 2 silent letters – E and G.
Why are there 2? Why not just 1 or 3?

There should, in fact, be more in –
There should be 4 in foreign.

REAL Skiers

REAL skiers get up at 3 just to go
Start up their cars for the slopes.
REAL skiers climb if the mountain has no
Gondolas, chairs, T's or ropes.

REAL skiers ski when it's frigid outside;
Sub-zero is one of those gifts.
Add on a layer, the cold will provide
Much shorter lines for the lifts.

REAL skiers ski and they suffer no pain,
Even when rain starts to fall.
'Cause the only thing worse than skiing in rain,
Is not skiing at all.

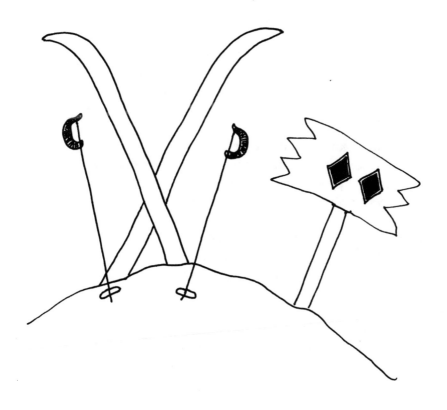

Nature's Awful Sounds

I hear the wind whistling through all the trees
And it plays like it has the most horrid disease.
But I know that the sound of the robin's song
Will sweeten the air and soothe me along.

And soon I can hear that old chirp-chirp-chirp,
But it sounds as grotesque as – well, burp-burp-burp.
Those were the sounds that once made me feel lucky.
Why do they now sound so awfully yucky?

My dad said he knew. Could it possibly be
That the world sounds so bad 'cause he just punished me?
And all 'cause I picked on my little brother.
He's always a pest in one way or another.

We were playing so nicely. Why did he spoil it
By giving my troll a swim in the toilet?
I yelled, "Hey that troll's more important than you.
Hold your breath, Troublemaker, you're going in, too."

I lowered him slowly, but soon had to stop
'Cause in walked my dad – man, did HE blow his top!
Now, I know I was wrong, but can't my dad see?
I can't last a whole evening without the TV.

Well, I s'pose just one night isn't TOO much trouble
For making my brother a scrubbing bubble.
So why have I filled my day with such sorrow?
My favorite shows – they're not on till tomorrow.

There, I feel better now. It's not so bad.
I might even stop throwing things at my dad.
Hey, all those birds – in the big maple tree.
They've cleaned up their act, they're no longer off-key.

And the crickets and bees give the air their fill.
They no longer sound like a dentist's drill.
And while I'm listening, I know, all along,
That they were alright and I was all wrong.

The Audition

I've got an audition for a very important play.
I've got an audition and it's coming up – today?
Omigosh, what'll I do?
I need an act that's fresh and new.
Omigosh, what'll I say,
To make them want me in this play?

I could show them I could act very quiet,
Shouting out my lines while I tip-toed.
Or I'll recite Lincoln's Gettysburg Address.
Oh no, I couldn't - I don't know the zip-code.

I've gotta think of SOMETHING I can show-off.
I just can't let them know I'm really stuck.
And then I'll practice, practice, practice, practice.
Uh - I'm on in thirty seconds, wish me luck.

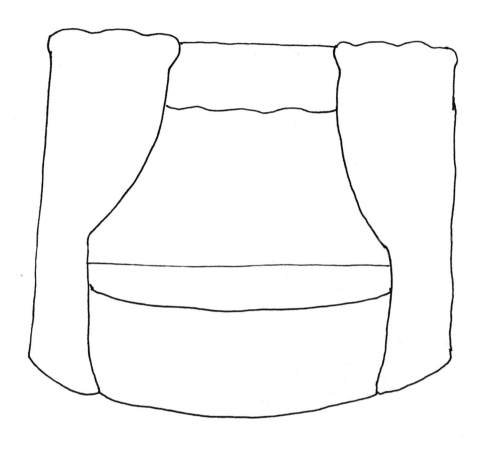

A Worm in My Apple

I got a shiny apple,
And it looked delish.
I went to take a bite
But dropped it on my dish.

I saw there was a hole
And you could bet
That I didn't want a worm
In my mouth just yet.

So I cut around the hole
And threw that away.
I looked around to see
Where Mr. Worm might stay.

I couldn't find him there
In that bottom perch
So I cut the apple's side
And kept up the search.

That did not expose
The little wormie yet,
So, off came another side
To find that squirmy pet.

Instead, all I found
Was an apple, so
I began to cut the top
To find my little foe.

With the top gone he
Would be an easy find,
So I looked all over
For that worm's behind.

I cut the last part
And began to call
"Where are you at
You little worm slimeball?"

That's the whole story
And there ain't no more,
'Cause the apple's gone;
I don't eat the core.

Borrowed Stuff

It's obvious that somebody
Keeps borrowing my stuff.
My hat is gone, my jacket, too.
Alright, enough's enough.

Yesterday, my special pen
It disappeared from sight.
And my new favorite pair of socks
Are also gone tonight.

Well, now I'm on a mission.
This is MY stuff, it's not his.
I'll look for where he has it
Then I'll find out who he is.

Imagine that! My special pen –
I found it tucked away,
Right where I was using it
For homework yesterday.

The socks weren't in my left shoe,
They were in the right, instead.
I found my hat and jacket
They were left behind my bed.

It's obvious this borrower
Takes all the things he's found,
And, carelessly, he drops them
As he follows me around.

A Tree in the Forest

If a tree falls in the forest
And no one was there, did it make a sound?
If a tree falls in the forest,
Who really cares, if no one's around?

This question has bothered some people for years,
Who clearly don't get how things work in our ears.

If a tree falls in the forest,
And no one is there, did it risk life and limb?
If a tree falls in the forest,
And someone is there, did the tree fall on him?

But the question of my parents,
Because they're convinced that they are all-knowing:
If a tree falls in the forest,
Why wasn't it looking where it was going?

Home from School

My tummy hurts, so does my head
And I just can't get out of bed.
No school for me, I feel half-dead.
I guess I'll be at home instead.

Don't worry, Mom, I'll be okay.
I'll find some things to do today.
I know I'm way too sick to play,
But I can get by, anyway.

I'll sleep a lot between TV
And then I'll crank the DVD.
For lunch a hot dog works for me.
And then, a candy bar or 3.

Yeah, soup is better, I'm aware,
But stay in bed? Mom, that's unfair.
And skip TV? You wouldn't dare.
I'll be fine, Mom, gosh, I swear.

You're the boss, Mom, you know best,
Okay, okay, I'll get some rest.
I promise I won't be a pest.
Just let me miss today's math test.

Amberly Tenney's Report Card

Hiya, Mom, my homework's done
And, gee, you look real nice.
I'm here to do the dishes now,
In fact, I'll do them twice.

Tomorrow's clothes are set for school,
And guess what else I did.
Why d'you say that something's up?
I'm just an awesome kid.

Uh, by the way, there's something
In my schoolbag I should show you.
Now, other folks might get upset.
Fort'nately, I know you.

As you'll soon see, I did real well
In almost every class.
It's just that needless subject – Math -
I almost didn't pass.

Extra problems? Show my work?
Don't get carried away.
I just fooled you big-time, mom.
See - I got an A.

The Secret

I just heard a secret at the baseball field.
I just heard a secret that will never be revealed.
I know you want to know it.
You think I'm gonna blow it?
I just heard a secret. Rest assured, my lips are sealed.

I know you'll try to get me to tell you if you can.
Don't bother with that candy, you can't bribe an honest man.
Put away the baseball cards. You've got a lot to learn.
Think that will make me lose the trust I've worked so hard to
earn?

Perhaps I didn't make myself altogether clear;
I just heard a secret and the secret's staying here.
If you gave me fifty dollars, I still would never say
That we just got playoff tickets, to go on your birthday.

Me Shoes

A dusty wind came blowing through.
I stopped, not knowing what to do.
Dare I risk dust upon me shoe?
Me shoes must be protected.

I couldn't run. I couldn't hide.
There was no house to go inside.
So panicked there, I could have died.
Me shoes must be protected.

Quickly, I took off me shirt
To save me shoes both from the dirt.
And thus concealed, they went unhurt.
Me shoes must be protected.

Me shirt around me ankles lay.
The wind came back the other way,
And took me shirt, I'm sad to say.
Me shoes must be protected.

More dust came in the wind by chance.
An unfortunate circumstance.
I'd nothing but to drop me pants.
Me shoes must be protected.

Half-naked there, I'd worked so hard,
So hard, me bloomin' shoes to guard.
Then came the crew from Scotland Yard.
Me shoes must be protected.

They made arrangements for me ruse,
Arrangements I could not refuse.
One cell for me, one for me shoes.
Me shoes must be protected.

Just Found a Wallet

Just found a wallet - by my mom's car.
I wasn't aware of whose it could have been.
I scooped it right up, thanked my lucky star,
And headed back home with the world's biggest grin.

I betcha I'm rich, I pondered right then.
I thought about all of the money inside.
I probably won't be this lucky again,
To find untold riches - to get a free ride.

The wallet was mine. Excited, I kissed it
And thought of how much money I would soon get.
But then I realized - someone else missed it;
Someone else out there was pretty upset.

That's when it hit me – it just wasn't right;
The wallet was not really my property.
However much money existing inside,
Must be returned with it, properly.

I opened the wallet to find out who
Abandoned such treasure. Egads, what a bum!
Its owner just might be somebody I knew.
I read my own name, and boy, I felt dumb.

A Physical Physical

It's been a year since last time, Doc.
I'm no longer a kid.
No, I don't want that shot – oops, sorry.
I sure hope YOU did.

Oh, here's that little hammer-thing.
You use it on my knee.
Hey, does it work the same on heads? Guess
Not on yours – sorry!

And, now you want me quiet, right?
So you'll hear my heartbeat?
HELLO, STETHOSCOPE – Hey, Doc,
Why'd you leave your feet?

The physical is over? Well,
I'm glad to hear I passed.
But last year took an hour. How come
This one went so fast?

You're looking rather gloomy, Doc.
Why the look of sorrow?
Tell ya what – I gotta run, but
I'll come back tomorrow!

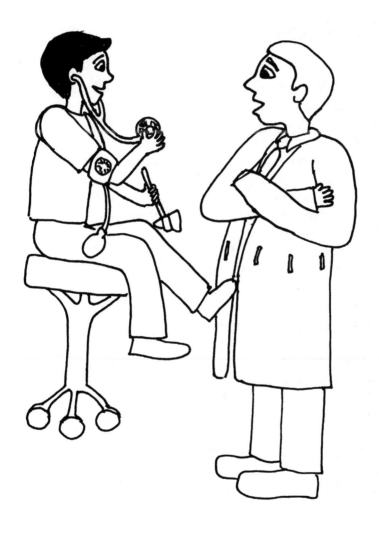

Didja Like It?

If you liked this book, please help me write another.
Here's what to do – kids, ask your dad or mother.

Try the "Say Nice Things" contest – so easy to do.
Everyone's a winner, and there's special prizes, too.

To enter, think of nice things to say about my poems
And e-mail your comments to friends' or cousins' homes.

From all those who e-mail, I'll select a set
Of semi-finalists and here's what they'll get:

Their comments are published for everybody's eyes,
And they're entered in a drawing for a great cash prize.

Those who get your e-mails will also win;
They learn about a book that has some laughs within.

You should send an e-mail. Come and take a look:
You'll also get a discount to use on my next book.

The next page has information in detail.
But everybody wins if you just e-mail.

How to get discounts and entered for cash prizes (through 2001):

What you do:
Send an e-mail to people you know – friends, relatives. (Sample e-mails are on the next page.) If you say something nice about this book, you copy me, jeff@chucklebooks.com, (either copy (cc) or blind copy (bcc)), and you include www.chucklebooks.com as a place to get the book, I will do some nice things for you.
Kids – never send e-mail to someone you don't know unless you check with your parents.

What I will do for you:

1. Send you a thank you poem.
2. Send you an e-coupon. The e-coupon is good for a discount off another copy of this book, should you want to send it as a gift, or it can be used on my next book. The amount of the discount depends on the number of people you address in the e-mail.
1 person	–	20% off
2 people	–	25% off
3 people	–	30% off
4 or more	–	40% off
3. Selected comments will be published on the website www.chucklebooks.com, along with the name and state of each person who wrote one of them.
4. The providers of those comments will be entered into the chucklebooks website drawing for cash prizes. For complete rules, see www.chucklebooks.com

If you have any questions, please e-mail them to jeff@chucklebooks.com

Example e-mails

Kids' example:

To: dingo@aols.com, frog@earthlinks.net, goat@moosepuppies.com, guppy@sea.com

Cc: jeff@chucklebooks.com

Subject: book recommendation

Hello, guys -
How y'all doing? I haven't heard from any of you in a while. I wanted to let you know about this book I just got called "There's a Hippo in My Locker". It has some really funny poems in it that made me laugh out loud. The poems are cool because adults just don't understand them like we kids do. It's available at bookstores and from www.chucklebooks.com
I hope you like the book as much as I do.
See ya.

Parents' example:

To: dingo@aols..com, frog@earthlinks.net, goat@moosepuppies.com, guppy@sea.com

Cc: jeff@chucklebooks.com

Subject: book recommendation

Hello, everybody -
I'm sending you this book recommendation e-mail for several reasons. First, my son, Billy, really loved the book "There's a Hippo in My Locker" by Jeff Nathan. It is humorous poetry from a kid's perspective that had us both laughing. At the back of the book is a contest that Billy wanted to enter because he liked the book so much. If he says something nice about the book in an e-mail, he gets entered. Here's what he had to say: "This book has the funniest poems I've ever seen. I've read the book three times already."
If you can't find the book at your favorite bookstore, you can get it www.chucklebooks.com
Best wishes to everyone.

Give the Gift of Chuckles

If you got this far, you enjoyed this book. Don't you think your cousin – niece – nephew – friend – grandparent – aunt - uncle – minister – rabbi – teacher – caddie – pet would enjoy it, too?

Check your favorite bookstore, order here, or go to:
www.chucklebooks.com

_____ copies *There's a Hippo in My Locker* $7.95   each
      U.S. shipping is $3.00   per address
      MA residents, please add tax of   39¢   per book

Enclosed is my check or money order for $_____

Charge: _____Visa   _____Mastercard

Name MADISON

Address 18 JESSE LN

City/State/Zip Taunton MA

Phone 508-880-6518   **e-mail** _____

Card # _____   **Exp. Date** 10/19/10

Signature _____

Please make check payable and mail to:
Chucklebooks
PO Box 1052
Andover, MA 01810

About the author

Jeff Nathan, shown here with his daughter, **Jillian Nathan**, who did the illustrations for this book, is a member of the Society of Children's Book Writer's & Illustrators. A poet, author, singer/songwriter and software marketing executive, he began writing poems for his own children's theatrical auditions. As other children started hearing and enjoying them, many asked if he would write a poem for them, too. Soon, he had the start of *There's a Hippo in My Locker*. In 1998, he began introducing his poetry to a number of schools in New England. Beginning a "Get Out Your Pens" program, Mr. Nathan brought his fun and effective messaging to school assemblies. He also found that his one-page "humorous children's perspectives in poems", were a great way to motivate some kids into reading. He lives in Andover, Massachusetts with his family.